S.M

KT-389-816

OBIN HOOD

RICHARD BRASSEY

First published in Great Britain in 2013
by Orion Children's Books
a division of the Orion Publishing Group Ltd
Orion House, 5 Upper St Martin's Lane, London WC2H 9EA
An Hachette UK company

10 9 8 7 6 5 4 3 2 1

Text and illustrations copyright © Richard Brassey 2013

A catalogue record for this book is available from the British Library

Printed in China

ISBN 978 1 4440 0129 7

www.orionbooks.co.uk

Long ago in the Middle Ages, minstrels sang
songs about an outlaw named Robin Hood.

The punishment for shooting one of the king's deer is to have your ears cut off!

Before the Normans came we Saxons could hunt deer and feast on venison as we pleased.

In the songs, Robin was a Saxon yeoman or small farmer who shot a deer for a bet. When the Normans had conquered England a hundred years earlier, they had declared one third of all the land to be Royal Forest where only the king could hunt. The deer Robin shot was on the king's land, so Robin became an outlaw.

Robin hid in Sherwood Forest, where he gathered a group of outlaws about him. They stole only from the ruthless Norman barons and bishops. Often they gave the money to the poor Saxons who the Normans forced to work in their fields and pay taxes to them.

Centuries later, when writers wrote down stories about Robin in expensive books, they changed him into a nobleman because they thought their posh readers wouldn't want to read about an ordinary yeoman.

Robin, they said, was really a half Norman/half Saxon noble, named Robert, who lived in swanky Loxley Hall. On the day of his wedding to Maid Marian, Prince John sent the Sheriff of Nottingham and Guy of Gisborne to arrest him.

ROBIN'S RANGE

Another confusion is that people in different parts of the country wanted Robin to be their local hero, so stories about him were set all over the place depending on who told them. Though most are in Nottingham or Yorkshire there are also scores of places with their own legends about Robin throughout England . . .

YORKSHIRE

ROBIN HOOD'S GRAVE

ROBIN HOOD'S WELL

DONCASTE

KIRKLEES PRIORY

BARNSDALE

LITTLE JOHN'S GRAVE

THE PEAK DISTRICT

LOXLEY HALL

ROBIN HOOD'S CAVE

ROBIN HOOD'S STRIDE

ROBIN HOOD'S
BAY

YORK MOORS

SCARBOROUGH

YORK

SHERWOOD
FOREST

LINCOLN

NORTH SEA

NOTTINGHAM
CASTLE

KING RICHARD
THE LIONHEART

In stories, Richard I was often said to be a good king. But he was always away fighting Crusades in Palestine, leaving his greedy younger brother, Prince John, to run England.

NASIR,
THE
SARACEN

BETTRIS

GEORGE
A GREEN

WILL
SCARLET

FRIAR
TUCK

ALAN A DALE

Robert was loyal to the Lionheart and so hated by Prince John. He escaped into the forest and changed his named to Robin. But whether you prefer posh Robin or yeoman Robin, the names of his merry men and the stories about them are often the same.

MUCH,
THE MILLER'S
SON

MAID MARIAN   ROBIN   LITTLE JOHN

All were equal in the greenwood, where they passed their days practising archery, fencing, playing quarterstaff, hunting, ambushing wealthy travellers and feasting merrily.

ROBIN'S ENEMIES

PRINCE JOHN
became king after his brother Richard. Such a bad ruler that the nobles forced him to sign the Magna Carta, giving up much of his power.

THE SHERIFF
the greedy representative of the king in Nottingham.

SIR GUY OF GISBORNE
a Norman who wished to marry Marian for her money.

The first merry man to join Robin was Will Scarlet. After Robin's escape to the forest, Will sneaked back to Loxley Hall with a boy named Much to collect Robin's jewels and money. But they were recognised and chased into the forest by Sir Guy. Will hid Much and the treasure in a hollow tree before he himself was caught and dragged to Nottingham.

Hearing Will was about to be hanged, Robin and his men secretly entered Nottingham. Robin, disguised as a pilgrim, asked if he could be the hangman. Then, cutting Will's bonds, he shot an arrow into the sheriff's hat. The merry men threw off their hoods and carried Will safely back to the forest.

One day in the forest, Robin was about to cross a footbridge when a large man carrying a staff stepped onto the other side. There wasn't room for them both, so Robin challenged him to a duel. After a long fight, the stranger knocked Robin into the stream. Robin blew his horn, and his merry men came running.

What's your name?

John Little.

Then we'll call you Little John!

Robin invited the stranger to join them in the forest.

I'll stop fighting if you join me. I am Robin Hood.

Is it really you, Robin?

Marian and Robin took part in an archery contest. Both shot arrows into the bullseye. Afterwards, Marian and a friar, named Tuck, got into a fight with the sheriff. So Marian became an outlaw too.

She slipped away from her father's home disguised as a young man. In the forest she met Robin, also in disguise. At first neither recognised the other and they fought a duel which neither could win.

Meanwhile, Friar Tuck returned to his hermitage by the river where he acted as a ferryman. One day, when Robin needed to cross, Tuck demanded money from him. Robin drew his sword and forced Tuck to carry him across on his shoulders. Tuck tipped Robin into the river. Robin laughed and that's how Friar Tuck became a merry man.

BLONDEL, THE MINSTREL

King Richard had disappeared while returning from the Crusades. His minstrel, Blondel, found him imprisoned in a German castle. A ransom needed paying for his release. Robin redoubled his efforts, stealing from the rich to help raise the money.

Prince John hated Robin for supporting Richard. He sent the sheriff and Sir Guy into the forest to capture him. Instead Robin killed Gisborne in a duel. Then a black knight rode up and helped Robin chase away the sheriff.

Ha! Right in his bottom!

To win popularity, Prince John decided to hold a tournament. John recognised Robin during the archery contest but dared not arrest him in front of the friendly crowd. John's champion archer hit the bullseye, but Robin's aim was so true he split the champion's arrow.

Robin is a real champion of the people!

Some time later, Robin met a pilgrim in the forest and invited him back to dinner. They arrived at the camp to find Prince John trying to kidnap Marian. When the pilgrim removed his hood, everybody fell to their knees for it was King Richard. Prince John fled back to Nottingham while the merry men feasted with their king.

The Black Knight was me too!

With the return of King Richard, Robin and Marian were married. After the wedding, some say Robin left for Palestine on a Crusade with the king. Others insist that he and Marian lived happily together at Loxley for five peaceful years.

But the king did leave for the Crusades again – where he was killed. Hearing rumours of his death, Robin went to Nottingham to seek news. Unfortunately the sheriff caught him, chained him in a high turret and bricked up the door. Robin thought he would die until he was able to work his chains loose and blow his horn. Little John heard it and shot an arrow through the window with a silk thread and a rope attached. Robin lowered himself to the ground but fell the last bit and hurt his back.

What do I do when I get to the end of the rope?

Jump?

It cannot be Robin. Must be a ghost! Aaaaahh!

Robin and Little John raced back to Loxley and collected Marian. Pursued through the forest, they turned to fight. The sheriff froze when he saw Robin because he thought Robin had died in the tower. Robin ran him through with his sword. Still the sheriff's men gave chase until Marian found sanctuary at Kirklees Priory.

Robin himself raced across the Yorkshire moors and escaped on a fishing ship at Scarborough. During the voyage, he helped the fishermen fight off French pirates. Eventually they landed him at the place in Yorkshire known ever since as Robin Hood's Bay, and he made his way back to Kirklees where Marian had become a nun.

But Robin had never really recovered from his fall. Marian and Little John nursed him as he lay dying. Calling for his bow, he shot one last strong arrow through the window into the greenwood, asking to be buried on the spot where it fell. Marian lived on to become abbess of the priory. When she died she was buried beside Robin.

But the legend of Robin was only just beginning. Robin Hood games, where revellers wore fancy dress, became popular at May Fairs in the Middle Ages.

Once Henry VIII and some of his nobles surprised Queen Catherine of Aragon in her chamber disguised as merry men. She pretended to believe Henry really was Robin Hood.

Guess who!

Eeek! It's Robin Hood.

Robin and his men were mentioned by Shakespeare and have been the subject of countless books, operas, video games and at least a hundred films and animated cartoons, not to mention TV shows. There's even been a Robin Hood in space!